[Madeleine Floyd]

Born in 1969, Madeleine Floyd studied
Fine Art and Illustration at Camberwell
College of Art, London, and has achieved
great success in both fields. Her illustrations,
watercolours and oil paintings are well known
and have been published and collected
around the world. She works from her garden
studio in London and has become one of
Britain's best-loved artists. A long-standing
appreciation of nature led to Madeleine
producing a sketchbook full of Birdsong
illustrations and this has since grown into a
successful range of beautiful licensed products.

Madeleine Floyd

A Year of Birdsong
2015 Diary

"Cheeep..... cheeep....." House Sparrow

Personal Details

Name

Address

Telephone: Home

Mobile

Work

E-mail

In emergency please contact:

Telephone

Useful Information

National Insurance no.

Driving licence no.

AA/RAC no.

Other Useful Numbers

Doctor	Dentist
Optician	Childminder
School	Vet
Bank	Building society
Train station	Bus station
Airport	Water
Plumber	Electrician
Gas	Electricity
Hairdresser	Garage
Taxi	Cinema

2015 Calendar

JANUARY
```
M  ·   5  12  19  26
T  ·   6  13  20  27
W  ·   7  14  21  28
T  1   8  15  22  29
F  2   9  16  23  30
S  3  10  17  24  31
S  4  11  18  25   ·
```

FEBRUARY
```
M  ·   2   9  16  23
T  ·   3  10  17  24
W  ·   4  11  18  25
T  ·   5  12  19  26
F  ·   6  13  20  27
S  ·   7  14  21  28
S  1   8  15  22   ·
```

MARCH
```
M  30   2   9  16  23
T  31   3  10  17  24
W   ·   4  11  18  25
T   ·   5  12  19  26
F   ·   6  13  20  27
S   ·   7  14  21  28
S   1   8  15  22  29
```

APRIL
```
M  ·   6  13  20  27
T  ·   7  14  21  28
W  1   8  15  22  29
T  2   9  16  23  30
F  3  10  17  24   ·
S  4  11  18  25   ·
S  5  12  19  26   ·
```

MAY
```
M  ·   4  11  18  25
T  ·   5  12  19  26
W  ·   6  13  20  27
T  ·   7  14  21  28
F  1   8  15  22  29
S  2   9  16  23  30
S  3  10  17  24  31
```

JUNE
```
M  1   8  15  22  29
T  2   9  16  23  30
W  3  10  17  24   ·
T  4  11  18  25   ·
F  5  12  19  26   ·
S  6  13  20  27   ·
S  7  14  21  28   ·
```

JULY
```
M  ·   6  13  20  27
T  ·   7  14  21  28
W  1   8  15  22  29
T  2   9  16  23  30
F  3  10  17  24  31
S  4  11  18  25   ·
S  5  12  19  26   ·
```

AUGUST
```
M  31   3  10  17  24
T   ·   4  11  18  25
W   ·   5  12  19  26
T   ·   6  13  20  27
F   ·   7  14  21  28
S   1   8  15  22  29
S   2   9  16  23  30
```

SEPTEMBER
```
M  ·   7  14  21  28
T  1   8  15  22  29
W  2   9  16  23  30
T  3  10  17  24   ·
F  4  11  18  25   ·
S  5  12  19  26   ·
S  6  13  20  27   ·
```

OCTOBER
```
M  ·   5  12  19  26
T  ·   6  13  20  27
W  ·   7  14  21  28
T  1   8  15  22  29
F  2   9  16  23  30
S  3  10  17  24  31
S  4  11  18  25   ·
```

NOVEMBER
```
M  30   2   9  16  23
T   ·   3  10  17  24
W   ·   4  11  18  25
T   ·   5  12  19  26
F   ·   6  13  20  27
S   ·   7  14  21  28
S   1   8  15  22  29
```

DECEMBER
```
M  ·   7  14  21  28
T  1   8  15  22  29
W  2   9  16  23  30
T  3  10  17  24  31
F  4  11  18  25   ·
S  5  12  19  26   ·
S  6  13  20  27   ·
```

2016 Calendar

JANUARY
```
M  ·   4  11  18  25
T  ·   5  12  19  26
W  ·   6  13  20  27
T  ·   7  14  21  28
F  1   8  15  22  29
S  2   9  16  23  30
S  3  10  17  24  31
```

FEBRUARY
```
M  1   8  15  22  29
T  2   9  16  23   ·
W  3  10  17  24   ·
T  4  11  18  25   ·
F  5  12  19  26   ·
S  6  13  20  27   ·
S  7  14  21  28   ·
```

MARCH
```
M  ·   7  14  21  28
T  1   8  15  22  29
W  2   9  16  23  30
T  3  10  17  24  31
F  4  11  18  25   ·
S  5  12  19  26   ·
S  6  13  20  27   ·
```

APRIL
```
M  ·   4  11  18  25
T  ·   5  12  19  26
W  ·   6  13  20  27
T  ·   7  14  21  28
F  1   8  15  22  29
S  2   9  16  23  30
S  3  10  17  24   ·
```

MAY
```
M  30   2   9  16  23
T  31   3  10  17  24
W   ·   4  11  18  25
T   ·   5  12  19  26
F   ·   6  13  20  27
S   ·   7  14  21  28
S   1   8  15  22  29
```

JUNE
```
M  ·   6  13  20  27
T  ·   7  14  21  28
W  1   8  15  22  29
T  2   9  16  23  30
F  3  10  17  24   ·
S  4  11  18  25   ·
S  5  12  19  26   ·
```

JULY
```
M  ·   4  11  18  25
T  ·   5  12  19  26
W  ·   6  13  20  27
T  ·   7  14  21  28
F  1   8  15  22  29
S  2   9  16  23  30
S  3  10  17  24  31
```

AUGUST
```
M  1   8  15  22  29
T  2   9  16  23  30
W  3  10  17  24  31
T  4  11  18  25   ·
F  5  12  19  26   ·
S  6  13  20  27   ·
S  7  14  21  28   ·
```

SEPTEMBER
```
M  ·   5  12  19  26
T  ·   6  13  20  27
W  ·   7  14  21  28
T  1   8  15  22  29
F  2   9  16  23  30
S  3  10  17  24   ·
S  4  11  18  25   ·
```

OCTOBER
```
M  31   3  10  17  24
T   ·   4  11  18  25
W   ·   5  12  19  26
T   ·   6  13  20  27
F   ·   7  14  21  28
S   1   8  15  22  29
S   2   9  16  23  30
```

NOVEMBER
```
M  ·   7  14  21  28
T  1   8  15  22  29
W  2   9  16  23  30
T  3  10  17  24   ·
F  4  11  18  25   ·
S  5  12  19  26   ·
S  6  13  20  27   ·
```

DECEMBER
```
M  ·   5  12  19  26
T  ·   6  13  20  27
W  ·   7  14  21  28
T  1   8  15  22  29
F  2   9  16  23  30
S  3  10  17  24  31
S  4  11  18  25   ·
```

December 2014

Monday
22

Tuesday
23

Wednesday   Christmas Eve
24

Thursday   Christmas Day (Holiday UK, R. of Ireland, USA, CAN, AUS, NZL)
25

Friday   Boxing Day, St Stephen's Day (Holiday UK, R. of Ireland, USA, CAN, AUS, NZL)
26

Saturday
27

Sunday
28

" Coor-li...........coorr-lii........." Curlew

"Coor-li.......coorr-lii......." Curlew

Curlew *(Numenius arquata)*

The curlew is Europe's largest wader and he is the owner of a memorable anthem. His song is throaty, loud and ponderous. His name derives from the sound of his call, 'Coo-li', which he repeats with an accelerating tempo. There is a definite haunting melancholy to his call that can often be heard for much of the year, long after other birds have put away their music. The sound seems to express beautifully the reflective nature of our coastal landscape and lonely moorland.

He arrives at his breeding ground in early spring and his song flights involve an impressive take-off and descent with uplifted wings that give an appearance of enviable weightlessness.

O curlew, cry no more in the air,
Or only to the water in the West;
Because your crying brings to my mind
Passion-dimmed eyes and long heavy hair
That was shaken out over my breast:
There is enough evil in the crying of wind.
W.B. YEATS

December 2014/January 2015

Monday
29

Tuesday
30

New Year's Eve

Wednesday
31

New Year's Day (Holiday UK, R. of Ireland, USA, CAN, AUS, NZL)

Thursday
1

Holiday (SCT, NZL)

Friday
2

Saturday
3

Sunday
4

January

Monday

5

Tuesday

6

Wednesday

7

Thursday

8

Friday

9

Saturday

10

Sunday

11

" Chup...chup..chup....tzoo-eee...." Greenfinch

NOTES

"Chup...chup..chup...tzoo-eee...." Greenfinch

Greenfinch *(Carduelis chloris)*

The elegant greenfinch visits open deciduous woods but can also be found in orchards, hedges and large town gardens. His tune is one of fine staccato trills, slightly metallic and thin in tone. His song is made up of a loud rapid twittering on one note, followed by four or five other musical notes, and at times it is delivered in flight.

The greenfinch is a sociable fellow and can nest in close proximity to another pair and, on occasion, they gather into large feeding flocks. A somewhat bulky nest of grass and twigs is usually built among thick bushes or dense tree branches and is lined with grass, hair and feathers.

Glory be to God for dappled things,
For skies of couple-colour as a brinded cow;
For rose-moles all in stipple upon trout that swim;
Fresh-firecoal chestnut-falls, finches' wings;
Landscape plotted and pieced, fold, fallow and plough,
And all trades, their gear and tackle and trim.
GERARD MANLEY HOPKINS

January

Monday
12

Tuesday
13

Wednesday
14

Thursday
15

Friday
16

Saturday
17

Sunday
18

January

Monday

Martin Luther King, Jr. Day (Holiday USA)

19

Tuesday

20

Wednesday

21

Thursday

22

Friday

23

Saturday

24

Sunday

Burns Night (SCT)

25

Mallard ....

Mallard ....

Mallard (*Anas platyrhynchos*)

The much-loved mallard is the duck of our childhood visits to the park and it is the female mallard's 'quack-quack' call that has now become the quintessential 'duck voice'.

This breed of duck nests throughout Europe and is mainly resident. The drake is a handsome fellow, with his proud yellow bill, bottle-green head, clerical white collar and burgundy chest. His bright orange legs are set far apart and to the back of his curvaceously heavy body, a position that encourages his amusing waddling walk on his wide webbed feet.

Mallards feed on seeds, aquatic insects and grain – that is, when they are not being fed on the contents of our bread bins!

The love of offspring's nature's general law,
From tigresses and cubs to ducks and ducklings;
There's nothing whets the beak, or arms the claw
Like an invasion of their babes and sucklings.
LORD GEORGE BYRON

January/February

Australia Day (Holiday AUS)

Monday
26

Tuesday
27

Wednesday
28

Thursday
29

Friday
30

Saturday
31

Sunday
1

February

Monday
2

Tuesday
3

Wednesday
4

Thursday
5

Friday   Waitangi Day (Holiday NZL)
6

Saturday
7

Sunday
8

" Tsweeep... tweep........" Yellow Wagtail

"Tsweeep... tweep......." Yellow Wagtail

Yellow Wagtail *(Motacilla flava)*

The yellow wagtail is one of our more beautiful and colourful summer visitors to Britain. He breeds in marshes, water meadows and in damp grassy fields. With his striking bright yellow under parts, green overcoat and black legs, this fellow has a loud, flat yet full voice with a song made up of brief repetitious chirping phrases.

The female builds the nest on the ground, usually concealed in a clump of grass, and adeptly lined with soft animal hair and small feathers. She feeds her young fledglings on small insects and invertebrates that she finds through constant foraging as she runs across the ground.

Little Trotty Wagtail, he went in the rain
And tittering, tottering sideways, he ne'er got straight again,
He stooped to get a worm and looked up to get a fly,
And then he flew away ere his feathers they were dry.
JOHN CLARE

February

Monday
9

Tuesday
10

Wednesday
11

Thursday
12

Friday
13

St Valentine's Day

Saturday
14

Sunday
15

February

Monday

16

Presidents' Day (Holiday USA)

Tuesday

17

Shrove Tuesday

Wednesday

18

Ash Wednesday

Thursday

19

Friday

20

Saturday

21

Sunday

22

" Pink-pink....pink-pink.....pink...." Blackbird

NOTES

"Pink - pink .....pink - pink .....pink...... Blackbird

Blackbird *(Turdus merula)*

Europe's most familiar bird, the blackbird, owns one of our best-loved songs. The confident, full-throated melody of his song is, for many, the soundtrack to the arrival of spring. As soon as green shoots are imminent, he bursts into tuneful chorus from dawn until dusk.

Originally a woodland bird, the blackbird is now a common visitor to the bird table and his mate happily builds a nest in surprisingly visible places such as windowsills, woodpiles and up drainpipes. The bright orange beak of the blackbird is especially well equipped to assist in pulling up earthworms and these are given by both parents to their young, along with caterpillars, berries and scraps.

Sing a song of sixpence, a pocket full of rye;
Four and twenty blackbirds baked in a pie.
When the pie was opened, the birds began to sing;
Was not that a dainty dish to set before a king.
NURSERY RHYME

Monday
23

Tuesday
24

Wednesday
25

Thursday
26

Friday
27

Saturday
28

St David's Day

Sunday
1

March

Monday

2

Tuesday

3

Wednesday

4

Thursday

5

Friday

6

Saturday

7

Sunday

Daylight Saving Time begins (CAN, USA)

8

"Teeeek - teek - tiooo........." Bullfinch

NOTES

"Teeeek - teek - tioooo............" Bullfinch

Bullfinch *(Pyrrhula pyrrhula)*

Easily recognisable by his black velvet cap and rosy pink chest, the bullfinch is actually a fairly quiet and unobtrusive bird and is sadly declining in presence. The male has a soft, distinctive, piped whistled call, a gentle but somewhat creaky song and a skill for mimicry, which helped make him a popular ornamental cage bird in the Victorian age.

The female bullfinch is chosen by the male and remains for life with her romantic spouse. She builds her cup nest of twigs lined with moss and grass towards the end of April, and the male loyally keeps her company as she waits for her first brood of the year to hatch.

Bother Bulleys, let us sing
From the dawn till evening! –
For we know not that we go not
When the day's pale pinions fold
Unto those who sang of old.
THOMAS HARDY

March

Commonwealth Day

Monday
9

Tuesday
10

Wednesday
11

Thursday
12

Friday
13

Saturday
14

Mother's Day (UK, R. of Ireland)

Sunday
15

March

Monday
16

Tuesday
17   St Patrick's Day (Holiday R. of Ireland, N. Ireland)

Wednesday
18

Thursday
19

Friday
20

Saturday
21

Sunday
22

"Chak - chak - chak..... chak - chak ......" Magpie

NOTES

"Chak - chak - chak..... chak - chak ....." Magpie

Magpie *(Pica Pica)*

The hard, chattering and jeering call of the magpie is unmistakable. His noisy speech contains a few musical notes but we usually associate this pirate with a raucous and barking call that at times sounds obtrusive and mechanical.

The magpie is a resident mischief, often seen in pairs or flocks and with the supposed habit of collecting glittering objects and hiding them. He also stands accused of sometimes poaching other birds' eggs and fledglings from neighbours' nests, which are eaten to satisfy his opportunistic appetite. Superstition surrounds this elegant and glossy bird, and rhymes dating back to the eighteenth century often mention him as a bad omen.

One for sorrow, two for joy;
Three for a girl, four for a boy;
Five for silver, six for gold;
Seven for a secret, never to be told;
Eight for a wish, nine for a kiss;
Ten for a bird that's best to miss.
NURSERY RHYME

March

Monday
23

Tuesday
24

Wednesday
25

Thursday
26

Friday
27

Saturday
28

British Summer Time begins / European Daylight Saving Time begins

Sunday
29

March/April

Monday
30

Tuesday
31

Wednesday
1

Thursday
2

Friday   Good Friday (Holiday UK, AUS, CAN, NZL)
3

Saturday
4

Sunday   Easter Sunday / Daylight Saving Time ends (NZL, AUS – except WA, NT, QLD)
5

" C oooo - coooo - coooo.. " Collared Dove

NOTES

"Coooo - coooo - coooo.." Collared Dove

Collared Dove *(Streptopelia decaocto)*

The collared dove originates from Turkey and has spread rapidly across Europe at a faster rate than any other recorded species. His song is a loud, repetitive 'coo'. Depending on one's mood, it has been described by some as mournful, monotonous and even irritating, while for others it offers comfort, calm and a reminder of early summer mornings.

Quite at ease with humans, this dove sets up home in city centres or town squares and is a regular guest at bird tables and windowsills, chancing upon man's goodwill and a free meal. His nest is built of dry twigs and rubbish arranged somewhat haphazardly in the branches of tall bushes or thickets.

An Ant who in a brook would drink
Fell off the bank. He tried
To swim, and felt his courage sink –
This ocean seemed so wide.
But for a Dove who flew above
He would have drowned and died.
The friendly Dove within her beak
A bridge of grass-stem bore:
On this the Ant, though worn and weak.
Contrived to reach the shore.
JEAN DE LA FONTAINE

April

Easter Monday (Holiday UK except SCT, R. of Ireland, CAN, AUS, NZL)

Monday

6

Tuesday

7

Wednesday

8

Thursday

9

Friday

10

Saturday

11

Sunday

12

April

Monday
13

Tuesday
14

Wednesday
15

Thursday
16

Friday
17

Saturday
18

Sunday
19

"Chip-chi-chirichirichiri".... Chaffinch

NOTES

"Chip-chi-chirichirichiri"......Chaffinch

Chaffinch *(Fringilla coelebs)*

The loud, cheerful song of the chaffinch is a welcome sign of a warmer season. The celebratory melody accelerates downward and usually ends with a wonderful flourish of notes before the song is repeated up to ten times a minute. The male sings loudly to mark out his breeding territory.

With his pinkish orange chest and his blue bonnet, the chaffinch enjoys woodland areas but is equally at home in town or village gardens. The male brings materials to the female for the nest, but it is the female who actually builds a beautifully constructed and compact nest in the fork of a tree using moss, lichen and spider webs.

Scream'd Chaffinch, 'Sweet, sweet, sweet!
Pretty lovey, come and meet me here!'
'Chaffinch,' quoth I, 'be dumb awhile, in fear
Thy darling prove no better than a cheat,
And never come, or fly when wintry days appear.'
Yet from a twig, with voice so big,
The little fowl his utterance did repeat.
WILLIAM ALLINGHAM

April

Monday
20

Tuesday
21

Earth Day

Wednesday
22

St George's Day

Thursday
23

Friday
24

Anzac Day

Saturday
25

Sunday
26

April/May

Monday   Holiday (AUS, NZL)

27

Tuesday

28

Wednesday

29

Thursday

30

Friday

1

Saturday

2

Sunday

3

"Tswit - tswit ...." Swallow

NOTES

_____

_____

_____

_____

_____

"Tswit - tswit ...." Swallow

Swallow *(Hirundo rustica)*

Eating and drinking as he flies, the swallow is rarely seen on the ground, preferring an almost constant airborne life. His voice is pleasant and twittering and his songs sound conversational and slightly squeaky with a limited tonal range.

The swallow is a keen and agile aviator, graceful and swooping in flight. I have fond memories of watching swallows in flock as they expertly ascend and glide in a manner that seems to illustrate the idea of reaping the rewards of hard endeavour.

The migratory swallow has midnight blue upper parts and creamy buff under parts. His throat and forehead are a regal red and he is best recognised by his long, fork-tailed streamer feathers.

Swallows travel to and fro,
And the great winds come and go,
And the steady breezes blow,
Bearing perfume, bearing love.
Breezes hasten, swallows fly,
Towered clouds forever ply,
And at noonday, you and I
See the same sunshine above.
ROBERT LOUIS STEVENSON

May

Holiday (UK, R. of Ireland)

Monday

4

Tuesday

5

Wednesday

6

Thursday

7

Friday

8

Saturday

9

Mother's Day (AUS, CAN, NZL, USA)

Sunday

10

May

Monday

11

Tuesday

12

Wednesday

13

Thursday

14

Friday

15

Saturday

16

Sunday

17

" tsee - tsee - tsee - tsisi tsisisisisisisi"..... Blue Tit.

"tsee - tsee - tsee -tsisi tsisisisisisi'si"... Blue Tit.

Blue Tit *(Parus caeruleus)*

Sporting a blue cap and proud yellow chest, the blue tit is a much-loved visitor to the garden. His song is loud and high-pitched and ends in a long, rapid trill.

Swooping in to a sudden stop on the bird table and often seen feeding upside down on peanut baskets, the bird's acrobatics and agility have earned our esteem. He can be found in gardens, parks and woodland. The female has similar plumage to the male and can lay up to 16 eggs in a single brood. Once the chicks have hatched, both parents work hard to keep their hungry offspring well fed with a constant supply of small caterpillars and other tasty morsels.

O for thy wings, sweet bird!
And soul of melody by being blest –
Like thee, my voice had stirred
Some dear remembrance in a weary breast.
But whither wouldst thou rove,
Bird of the airy wing, and fold thy plumes?
In what dark leafy grove
Wouldst chant thy vespers 'mid rich glooms?
MARY BAKER EDDY

May

Victoria Day (Holiday CAN)

Monday
18

Tuesday
19

Wednesday
20

Thursday
21

Friday
22

Saturday
23

Sunday
24

May

Monday

Holiday (UK) / Memorial Day (Holiday USA)

25

Tuesday

26

Wednesday

27

Thursday

28

Friday

29

Saturday

30

Sunday

31

"Tuc - tuc - tuc ... " Sedge Warbler

NOTES

Sedge Warbler *(Acrocephalus schoenobaenus)*

The sedge warbler is a summer migrant who lives at the edges of our ponds and riverbeds and can also be found amongst our boggy marshlands. His song is sung with determination and is often interspersed with impersonations of other birds, blended together with warbles, trills, whistles and whirring musical notes to create a varied arrangement. An elusive fellow, he prefers to keep a low profile in amongst the reeds and grasses and is olive-brown in colour, with a cream stripe above his eyes.

During courtship the male makes impressive display flights, ascending in song and then spiralling down, descending with both his wings and tail feathers fanned out to impress his intended mate.

The breeze on the brae is mournfully blowing!
The brook in the hollow is plaintively flowing,
The warblers, the soul of the groves, are moaning,
For MacCrimmon that's gone, with no hope of returning!
DR NORMAN MACLEOD

June

Holiday (R. of Ireland) / Queen's Birthday (Holiday NZL)

Monday
1

Tuesday
2

Wednesday
3

Thursday
4

Friday
5

Saturday
6

Sunday
7

June

Monday

8

Tuesday

9

Wednesday

10

Thursday

11

Friday

12

Saturday

13

Sunday

14

"Gah — gah — gah ... gah ...." Herring Gull

NOTES

"Gah-gah-gah...gah....." Herring Gull

Herring Gull *(Larus argentatus)*

Herring gulls have a reputation for being scavengers, and certainly anyone enjoying a picnic on the beach usually doesn't have to wait long until a large, noisy gull begins to circle.

They are found on our rocky coasts and further inland, especially during winter, and are adept at dropping their chosen meal onto a hard surface in order to crack it open and reveal the tasty morsel within. They have heavy, slightly hooked bills marked with a red spot and they prefer to live on rocky coasts, where they nest on low-lying cliffs.

On the clefts of the wave-washed rock I sit,
When the ocean is roaring and raving nigh;
On the howling tempest I scream and flit,
With the storm in my wing, and the gale in my eye.
JOHN GARDINER CALKINS BRAINARD

June

Monday
15

Tuesday
16

Wednesday
17

Thursday
18

Friday
19

Saturday
20

Father's Day (UK, CAN, USA)

Sunday
21

June

Monday
22

Tuesday
23

Wednesday
24

Thursday
25

Friday
26

Saturday
27

Sunday
28

" Cuc-coo ... cuc-cooo .. " Cuckoo

NOTES

"Cuc-coo .... cuc-cooo ..." Cuckoo

Cuckoo (*Cuculus canorus*)

From the middle of April, you can hear the unmistakably melodious call of the male cuckoo. His loud, rich and throaty song is unique, reminiscent of a human mother affectionately calling to her children, which perhaps explains our love for him. Strangely, the female emits a loud bubbling call after laying an egg or during courtship.

Even in Chaucer's time, the 'Cokkow' was renowned for his fine anthem, and many old customs involve the capture of a cuckoo in return for an extension of good weather. Nevertheless, the cuckoo's sweet crooning belies its incredibly anti-social behaviour, as the female cuckoo roughly ousts innocent songbird eggs from their nests, replacing them with her own.

O blithe newcomer! I have heard,
I hear thee and rejoice:
O Cuckoo! Shall I call thee bird,
Or but a wandering Voice?
WILLIAM WORDSWORTH

June/July

Monday
29

Tuesday
30

Canada Day (Holiday CAN)

Wednesday
1

Thursday
2

Holiday (USA)

Friday
3

Independence Day (USA)

Saturday
4

Sunday
5

July

Monday

6

Tuesday

7

Wednesday

8

Thursday

9

Friday

10

Saturday

11

Sunday   Battle of the Boyne

12

"Tseeep - pseep ...." Meadow Pipit

NOTES

"Tseeep - pseep ...." Meadow Pipit

Meadow Pipit *(Anthus pratensis)*

The meadow pipit is adaptable in his choice of home, living at
an extremely wide range of altitudes. The courting male makes
impressive song flights, rising rapidly before gliding to the ground still
singing all the while. His fast piping song increases as he rises then
slows on descent, before ending with a trill on landing.

Like the skylark this fellow is rather nondescript in appearance with
brown and grey streaks and is often only distinguished by the unusually
long hind claw on his orange-brown legs. Despite his attempts to
conceal his nest, the meadow pipit is a favourite prey of the cuckoo
and often has his own eggs ousted by the garrulous intruder.

Come, on wings of joy we'll fly
To where my bower hangs on high;
Come, and make thy calm retreat
Among green leaves and blossoms sweet.
WILLIAM BLAKE

July

Holiday (N. Ireland)

Monday
13

Tuesday
14

Wednesday
15

Thursday
16

Friday
17

Saturday
18

Sunday
19

July

Monday
20

Tuesday
21

Wednesday
22

Thursday
23

Friday
24

Saturday
25

Sunday
26

"Wheeet .... wheet .... tuc-tuc ...." Nightingale

NOTES

"Wheeet.... wheet .... tuc-tuc .... " Nightingale

Nightingale *(Luscinia megarhynchos)*

The elusive nightingale is more often heard than seen.
A master of timing, he has a flutey song that is unquestionably
beautiful, offering variations in pitch and tempo interspersed with
guttural croaking and chuckling sounds. He usually performs
after dark and can use up to 250 different phrases in his song.
Each recital is made up of a unique composition, which has
earned him his reputation as one of Europe's
most impressive songsters.

When first we hear the shy-come nightingales,
They seem to mutter o'er their songs in fear,
And, climb we ere so soft the spinney rails,
All stops as if no bird was anywhere.
JOHN CLARE

July/August

Monday
27

Tuesday
28

Wednesday
29

Thursday
30

Friday
31

Saturday
1

Sunday
2

August

Monday

Holiday (SCT, R. of Ireland)

3

Tuesday

4

Wednesday

5

Thursday

6

Friday

7

Saturday

8

Sunday

9

"Charrr....charrr......." Dartford Warbler

Dartford Warbler *(Sylvia undata)*

Unlike his fellow warblers, the Dartford warbler braves cold winters and remains in Britain rather than escaping to warmer climates. As a result, this secretive and elusive bird is susceptible to decline but he can still be found on the dry lowland heaths of Hampshire and Dorset. His song is a quick, chattering warble, containing some brighter notes, but is usually sung at a fairly low pitch and often in flight.

A smart little fellow, he weighs no more than a wren, but has an impressively long, cocked tail that is half of his overall length. He sports a deep reddish-brown chest and a red eye ring that looks like a rather distinguished monocle.

*At half-past three a single bird
Unto a silent sky
Propounded but a single term
Of cautious melody.
At half-past four, experiment
Had subjugated test,
And lo! her silver principle
Supplanted all the rest.*
EMILY DICKINSON

August

Monday
10

Tuesday
11

Wednesday
12

Thursday
13

Friday
14

Saturday
15

Sunday
16

August

Monday
17

Tuesday
18

Wednesday
19

Thursday
20

Friday
21

Saturday
22

Sunday
23

"Tchikkk....." "Great Spotted Woodpecker

"Tchikkk...." "Great Spotted Woodpecker"

Great Spotted Woodpecker *(Dendrocopos major)*

An elegant chap, the great spotted woodpecker has a red cap
and white epaulettes that stand out against his smart black
jacket and buff under parts. Equally at home in coniferous
and deciduous woodland, both male and female birds are
known for their impressive drum rolling as they hammer
their bills against branches, often using their tails to grip
and as balancing anchors as they tap away.

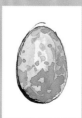

*The woodpecker pecked out a little round hole
And made him a house in a telephone pole.
One day when I watched he poked out his head,
And he had on a hood and a collar of red.
When the streams of rain pour out of the sky,
And the sparkles of lightning go flashing by,
And the big, big wheels of thunder roll,
He can snuggle back in the telephone pole.*
ELIZABETH MADOX ROBERTS

August

Monday
24

Tuesday
25

Wednesday
26

Thursday
27

Friday
28

Saturday
29

Sunday
30

Monday

Holiday (UK except SCT)

31

Tuesday

1

Wednesday

2

Thursday

3

Friday

4

Saturday

5

Sunday

Father's Day (AUS, NZL)

6

"Kirrri-kirrri-kirrri...." Common Tern.

NOTES

"Kircri-kircri-kircri...." Common Tern;

Common Tern *(Sterna hirundo)*

Despite its name, the common tern is not actually the most widespread member of its family, but it is certainly the one most likely to be seen and heard along our coasts, rivers and inland reservoirs. It has even been known to venture inland as far as London.

The common tern's long elegant tail has earned it the nickname 'sea-swallow' and it is a delight to watch its graceful flight and to see it hover over water before plunging down for an unlucky fish.

The fish in the water is silent,
the animal on the earth is noisy,
the bird in the air is singing,
But Man has in him the silence of the sea,
the noise of the earth and the music of the air.
RABINDRANATH TAGORE

September

Labor Day (Holiday USA) / Labour Day (Holiday CAN)

Monday
7

Tuesday
8

Wednesday
9

Thursday
10

Friday
11

Saturday
12

Sunday
13

September

Monday
14

Tuesday
15

Wednesday
16

Thursday
17

Friday
18

Saturday
19

Sunday
20

" Churr....churr....chnurrrrr....." Nightjar

NOTES

_____

_____

_____

_____

_____

"Churrr...churrr...chuurrrrr......" Nightjar

Nightjar *(Caprimulgus europaeus)*

The nightjar is so named because he sings by night. His
rapid whirring-jarring chant has been described by some as
sounding almost like a small engine revving up with intent.
It contains up to 40 notes per second and rises and falls in
pitch and tempo before slowing down towards the end as
if somewhat exhausted by its initial gusto. Usually the dry
throaty noises are delivered from a branch on which the
nightjar sits lengthwise, unlike most other birds who would
choose to sit perpendicular to their perch. During the day the
nightjar is well disguised and he lies low, taking rest along the
ground, which makes him a hard fellow to spot.

We are fully woven for summer
In stuff of limpest green,
The twitterer and the hummer
Here rest of nights, unseen,
While like a long-roll drummer
The nightjar thrills the treen.
THOMAS HARDY

September

UN International Day of Peace

Monday

21

Tuesday

22

Wednesday

23

Thursday

24

Friday

25

Saturday

26

Daylight Saving Time begins (NZL)

Sunday

27

September/October

Monday
28

Tuesday
29

Wednesday
30

Thursday
1

Friday
2

Saturday
3

Sunday   World Animal Day / Daylight Saving Time begins (AUS – except WA, NT, QLD)
4

"Pee-oo pee-oo ... Pee-ooo skairrk " .... Jay

"Pee-oo pee-oo..... Pee-ooo skairrk".......Jay

Jay *(Garrulus glandarius)*

The raucous, laughing call of the jay and his striking pink and chequered blue and black plumage are hard to miss. He is a skilled mimic and can imitate all kinds of other sounds, often to his own advantage, impersonating larger birds and other animals to ward off unwelcome woodland visitors.

Found across Europe, the jay roams the countryside, preferring oak woodland for his home. In autumn, he hops across the fallen leaves collecting acorns, carrying them in a pouch under his throat and burying hundreds beneath dry leaves and soil in preparation for the cold months ahead. Indeed the acorns that he forgets to retrieve contribute significantly to the spread of our own much-loved oak trees.

And as the sun breaks through the darkest clouds,
So honor peereth in the meanest habit.
What, is the jay more precious than the lark,
Because his feathers are more beautiful?
WILLIAM SHAKESPEARE

October

Monday
5

Tuesday
6

Wednesday
7

Thursday
8

Friday
9

Saturday
10

Sunday
11

October

Monday 12	Columbus Day (Holiday USA) / Thanksgiving Day (Holiday CAN)

Tuesday

13

Wednesday

14

Thursday

15

Friday

16

Saturday

17

Sunday

18

" Chit - chit - chiti - tzerrr......" Wren

NOTES

_____

_____

_____

_____

_____

"Chit-chit-chiti-tzerrr......" Wren

Wren *(Troglodytes troglodytes)*

A living adage to the saying that size is not everything, the diminutive wren is a most determined and impressive singer and his boisterous and full-throated warbling song can be heard loudly across the seasons. His song is shrill and is delivered with real gusto. One of Europe's smallest birds, the wren spends most of his time on or near the ground.
A sociable creature, it roosts in groups and is often found in gardens, woodland undergrowth or thickets beside ditches and streams. In spring, the male uses plant stalks, twigs and moss to build a number of spherical nests, the female takes her pick and the new home is finished inside with soft hair and feathers.

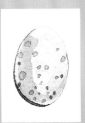

Among the dwelling framed by birds
In field or forest with nice care,
Is none that with the little Wren's
In snugness may compare.
WILLIAM WORDSWORTH

October

Monday
19

Tuesday
20

Wednesday
21

Thursday
22

Friday
23

Saturday
24

British Summer Time ends / European Daylight Saving Time ends

Sunday
25

October/November

Monday   Holiday (R. of Ireland) / Labour Day (Holiday NZL)

26

Tuesday

27

Wednesday

28

Thursday

29

Friday

30

Saturday   Hallowe'en

31

Sunday   Daylight Saving Time ends (CAN, USA)

1

" Kleeep - a - kleeep .... kleeep - a - kleeep .. Oystercatcher "

"Kleeep-a-kleeep..... Kleeep-a-kleeep." Oystercatcher

Oystercatcher *(Haematopus ostralegus)*

The stout oystercatcher is bold in voice and body. He is often seen probing the shores with his red bill for cockles and mussels but has rarely been seen to polish off an oyster, despite his name. They congregate in numbers, and their brash ways and enormous tight flocks create, en masse, an incredibly loud chorus of strident piping trills. During courtship, this fellow can be seen running along the sand behind or beside his intended mate in the hope of winning her affection and deterring his rivals.

Lonely the seabird lies at her rest,
Blown like a down-blenched parcel of spray
Upon the wind, or follows her prey
Under a great wave's hollowing crest.
W.B. YEATS

WEEK 45

November

Monday
2

Tuesday
3

Wednesday
4

Bonfire Night

Thursday
5

Friday
6

Saturday
7

Remembrance Sunday (UK)

Sunday
8

November

Monday
9

Tuesday
10

Wednesday   Remembrance Day (Holiday CAN) / Veterans' Day (Holiday USA)
11

Thursday
12

Friday
13

Saturday
14

Sunday
15

"Korrk-kok .... korrrk-kok..." Pheasant

_____

_____

_____

_____

_____

"Korrk-kok .... Korrrk-kok.." Pheasant

Pheasant *(Phasianus colchicus)*

Our best-known resident game bird was introduced to Britain
from Asia in Roman times, though the current population is
largely the result of large-scale rearing in captivity for release
into the wild for game shooting. A debonair fellow,
the male has a long, slender and tapering tail, held clear off
the ground and often cocked upwards. He is dressed in the
palette of autumn with a greenish-blue head and glossy,
conker-coloured chest feathers with ink-black markings.

He marked a pheasant, as she stood
Upon a bank, above her brood;
With pride maternal beat her breast
As she harangued and led from nest:
'Play on, my infant brood – this glen
Is free from bad marauding men.
O trust the hawk, and trust the kite,
Sooner than man – detested wight!'
JOHN GAY

November

Monday
16

Tuesday
17

Wednesday
18

Thursday
19

Friday
20

Saturday
21

Sunday
22

November

Monday

23

Tuesday

24

Wednesday

25

Thursday   Thanksgiving Day (Holiday USA)

26

Friday

27

Saturday

28

Sunday

29

"Tchuck ... tchick ... tchiick ....." Song Thrush

NOTES

"Tchuck ... tchick ... tchiick ....." Song Thrush

Song Thrush *(Turdus philomelos)*

The migratory song thrush can be found across Europe in
gardens, woodland and grasslands. With the onset of colder
weather the song thrush flies off to its winter quarters, usually
in northern Africa or southern Europe. So named on account
of his loud and exuberant song, the song thrush sings a popular,
flutey melody. In spring he builds a grassy cup nest usually low
in bushes or hedgerows and he lines it with mud and dung both
cemented by saliva. Between three and five eggs are laid and the
young are fed on worms, snails, slugs and berries.

That's the wise thrush; he sings each song twice over,
Lest you should think he never could recapture
The first fine careless rapture!
ROBERT BROWNING

November/December

St Andrew's Day

Monday
30

Tuesday
1

Wednesday
2

Thursday
3

Friday
4

Saturday
5

Sunday
6

December

Monday
7

Tuesday
8

Wednesday
9

Thursday
10

Friday
11

Saturday
12

Sunday
13

"Tik-ik-ik....Tik..iki......" Robin

NOTES

"Tik-ik-ik...Tik...iki....." Robin

Robin *(Erithacus rubecula)*

The robin's song is beautiful and joyous and is sung with all his
heart and soul. He is one of the few birds whose song can be heard
virtually all year round and he will happily perform his sweet
warbling song at dusk. In Britain he has become the gardener's
companion, swooping down to dine on worms in the dug soil and
he is often quite aggressive in defence of his territory.

*Beautiful robin! with thy feathers red
Contrasting sweetly with the soft green tree,
Making thy little flights as thou art led
By things that tempt a simple one like thee –
I would that thou couldst warble me to tears
As lightly as the birds of other years.*
NATHANIEL PARKER WILLIS

December

Monday
14

Tuesday
15

Wednesday
16

Thursday
17

Friday
18

Saturday
19

Sunday
20

December

Monday
21

Tuesday
22

Wednesday
23

Thursday   Christmas Eve
24

Friday   Christmas Day (Holiday UK, R. of Ireland, USA, CAN, AUS, NZL)
25

Saturday   Boxing Day, St Stephen's Day
26

Sunday
27

Holiday (UK, R. of Ireland, CAN, AUS, NZL)

Monday

28

Tuesday

29

Wednesday

30

New Year's Eve

Thursday

31

New Year's Day (Holiday UK, R. of Ireland, USA, CAN, AUS, NZL)

Friday

1

Saturday

2

Sunday

3

2016 Planner

JANUARY		FEBRUARY		MARCH	
1	F	1	M	1	T
2	S	2	T	2	W
3	S	3	W	3	T
4	M	4	T	4	F
5	T	5	F	5	S
6	W	6	S	6	S
7	T	7	S	7	M
8	F	8	M	8	T
9	S	9	T	9	W
10	S	10	W	10	T
11	M	11	T	11	F
12	T	12	F	12	S
13	W	13	S	13	S
14	T	14	S	14	M
15	F	15	M	15	T
16	S	16	T	16	W
17	S	17	W	17	T
18	M	18	T	18	F
19	T	19	F	19	S
20	W	20	S	20	S
21	T	21	S	21	M
22	F	22	M	22	T
23	S	23	T	23	W
24	S	24	W	24	T
25	M	25	T	25	F
26	T	26	F	26	S
27	W	27	S	27	S
28	T	28	S	28	M
29	F	29	M	29	T
30	S			30	W
31	S			31	T

APRIL		MAY		JUNE	
1	F	1	S	1	W
2	S	2	M	2	T
3	S	3	T	3	F
4	M	4	W	4	S
5	T	5	T	5	S
6	W	6	F	6	M
7	T	7	S	7	T
8	F	8	S	8	W
9	S	9	M	9	T
10	S	10	T	10	F
11	M	11	W	11	S
12	T	12	T	12	S
13	W	13	F	13	M
14	T	14	S	14	T
15	F	15	S	15	W
16	S	16	M	16	T
17	S	17	T	17	F
18	M	18	W	18	S
19	T	19	T	19	S
20	W	20	F	20	M
21	T	21	S	21	T
22	F	22	S	22	W
23	S	23	M	23	T
24	S	24	T	24	F
25	M	25	W	25	S
26	T	26	T	26	S
27	W	27	F	27	M
28	T	28	S	28	T
29	F	29	S	29	W
30	S	30	M	30	T
		31	T		

2016 Planner

JULY		AUGUST		SEPTEMBER	
1	F	1	M	1	T
2	S	2	T	2	F
3	S	3	W	3	S
4	M	4	T	4	S
5	T	5	F	5	M
6	W	6	S	6	T
7	T	7	S	7	W
8	F	8	M	8	T
9	S	9	T	9	F
10	S	10	W	10	S
11	M	11	T	11	S
12	T	12	F	12	M
13	W	13	S	13	T
14	T	14	S	14	W
15	F	15	M	15	T
16	S	16	T	16	F
17	S	17	W	17	S
18	M	18	T	18	S
19	T	19	F	19	M
20	W	20	S	20	T
21	T	21	S	21	W
22	F	22	M	22	T
23	S	23	T	23	F
24	S	24	W	24	S
25	M	25	T	25	S
26	T	26	F	26	M
27	W	27	S	27	T
28	T	28	S	28	W
29	F	29	M	29	T
30	S	30	T	30	F
31	S	31	W		

2016 Planner

OCTOBER	NOVEMBER	DECEMBER
1 S	1 T	1 T
2 S	2 W	2 F
3 M	3 T	3 S
4 T	4 F	4 S
5 W	5 S	5 M
6 T	6 S	6 T
7 F	7 M	7 W
8 S	8 T	8 T
9 S	9 W	9 F
10 M	10 T	10 S
11 T	11 F	11 S
12 W	12 S	12 M
13 T	13 S	13 T
14 F	14 M	14 W
15 S	15 T	15 T
16 S	16 W	16 F
17 M	17 T	17 S
18 T	18 F	18 S
19 W	19 S	19 M
20 T	20 S	20 T
21 F	21 M	21 W
22 S	22 T	22 T
23 S	23 W	23 F
24 M	24 T	24 S
25 T	25 F	25 S
26 W	26 S	26 M
27 T	27 S	27 T
28 F	28 M	28 W
29 S	29 T	29 T
30 S	30 W	30 F
31 M		31 S

Names & Addresses

Name

Address

Postcode

Telephone   Mobile

E-mail

Name

Address

Postcode

Telephone   Mobile

E-mail

Name

Address

Postcode

Telephone   Mobile

E-mail

Name

Address

Postcode

Telephone   Mobile

E-mail

Name

Address

Postcode

Telephone   Mobile

E-mail

Name

Address

Postcode

Telephone   Mobile

E-mail

Names & Addresses

Name

Address

Postcode

Telephone   Mobile

E-mail

Name

Address

Postcode

Telephone   Mobile

E-mail

Name

Address

Postcode

Telephone   Mobile

E-mail

Name

Address

Postcode

Telephone   Mobile

E-mail

Name

Address

Postcode

Telephone   Mobile

E-mail

Name

Address

Postcode

Telephone   Mobile

E-mail

Names & Addresses

Name

Address

Postcode

Telephone   Mobile

E-mail

Name

Address

Postcode

Telephone   Mobile

E-mail

Name

Address

Postcode

Telephone   Mobile

E-mail

Name

Address

Postcode

Telephone   Mobile

E-mail

Name

Address

Postcode

Telephone   Mobile

E-mail

Name

Address

Postcode

Telephone   Mobile

E-mail

Names & Addresses

Name

Address

Postcode

Telephone   Mobile

E-mail

Name

Address

Postcode

Telephone   Mobile

E-mail

Name

Address

Postcode

Telephone   Mobile

E-mail

Name

Address

Postcode

Telephone   Mobile

E-mail

Name

Address

Postcode

Telephone   Mobile

E-mail

Name

Address

Postcode

Telephone   Mobile

E-mail

Notes

Notes

Notes